2022

JANUARY

M	T	W	T	F	S	S
					1	2
3	4	5	6	7	8	9
10	11	12	13	14	15	16
17	18	19	20	21	22	23
24	25	26	27	28	29	30
31						

FEBRUARY

M	T	W	T	F	S	S
	1	2	3	4	5	6
7	8	9	10	11	12	13
14	15	16	17	18	19	20
21	22	23	24	25	26	27
28						

MARCH

M	T	W	T	F	S	S
	1	2	3	4	5	6
7	8	9	10	11	12	13
14	15	16	17	18	19	20
21	22	23	24	25	26	27
28	29	30	31			

APRIL

M	T	W	T	F	S	S
				1	2	3
4	5	6	7	8	9	10
11	12	13	14	15	16	17
18	19	20	21	22	23	24
25	26	27	28	29	30	

MAY

M	T	W	T	F	S	S
						1
2	3	4	5	6	7	8
9	10	11	12	13	14	15
16	17	18	19	20	21	22
23	24	25	26	27	28	29
30	31					

JUNE

M	T	W	T	F	S	S
		1	2	3	4	5
6	7	8	9	10	11	12
13	14	15	16	17	18	19
20	21	22	23	24	25	26
27	28	29	30			

JULY

M	T	W	T	F	S	S
				1	2	3
4	5	6	7	8	9	10
11	12	13	14	15	16	17
18	19	20	21	22	23	24
25	26	27	28	29	30	31

AUGUST

M	T	W	T	F	S	S
1	2	3	4	5	6	7
8	9	10	11	12	13	14
15	16	17	18	19	20	21
22	23	24	25	26	27	28
29	30	31				

SEPTEMBER

M	T	W	T	F	S	S
			1	2	3	4
5	6	7	8	9	10	11
12	13	14	15	16	17	18
19	20	21	22	23	24	25
26	27	28	29	30		

OCTOBER

M	T	W	T	F	S	S
					1	2
3	4	5	6	7	8	9
10	11	12	13	14	15	16
17	18	19	20	21	22	23
24	25	26	27	28	29	30
31						

NOVEMBER

M	T	W	T	F	S	S
	1	2	3	4	5	6
7	8	9	10	11	12	13
14	15	16	17	18	19	20
21	22	23	24	25	26	27
28	29	30				

DECEMBER

M	T	W	T	F	S	S
			1	2	3	4
5	6	7	8	9	10	11
12	13	14	15	16	17	18
19	20	21	22	23	24	25
26	27	28	29	30	31	

ESSENTIALS

AT HOGWARTS

ADVANCE PLANNER

January

February

March

April

May

June

ADVANCE PLANNER

July

August

September

October

November

December

JANUARY

Things to do this month

Goals

Notes

Monday
27

Tuesday
28

Wednesday
29

Thursday
30

DEC 21/JAN 22

Friday
31

Saturday
1

New Year's Day

Sunday
2

Notes

JANUARY

Monday
3

New Year's Day Holiday
....

Tuesday
4

Bank Holiday (Scotland)
....

Wednesday
5

....

Thursday
6

JANUARY

Friday
7

Saturday
8

Sunday
9

Notes

JANUARY

Monday
10

Tuesday
11

Wednesday
12

Thursday
13

JANUARY

Friday
14

Saturday
15

Sunday
16

Notes

JANUARY

Monday
17

Tuesday
18

Wednesday
19

Thursday
20

JANUARY

Notes

JANUARY

Monday
24

Tuesday
25

Wednesday
26

Thursday
27

JANUARY

Friday
28

Saturday
29

Sunday
30

Notes

FEBRUARY

Things to do this month

Goals

Notes

JAN/FEB

Monday
31

Tuesday
1

chinese New Year (Tiger)

Wednesday
2

Thursday
3

FEBRUARY

Friday
4

Saturday
5

Sunday
6

Notes

FEBRUARY

Monday
7

Tuesday
8

Wednesday
9

Thursday
10

FEBRUARY

Friday
11

Saturday
12

Sunday
13

Notes

FEBRUARY

Monday
14

valentine's Day

Tuesday
15

Wednesday
16

Thursday
17

FEBRUARY

Friday
18

Saturday
19

Sunday
20

Notes

FEBRUARY

Monday
21

Tuesday
22

Wednesday
23

Thursday
24

FEBRUARY

Friday
25

Saturday
26

Sunday
27

Notes

MARCH

Things to do this month

Goals

Notes

FEB/MAR

Monday
28

Tuesday
1

St. David's Day (Wales) / Shrove Tuesday

Wednesday
2

o

Thursday
3

MARCH

Friday
4

Saturday
5

Sunday
6

Notes

MARCH

Monday
7

Tuesday
8

Wednesday
9

Thursday
10

MARCH

Friday
11

Saturday
12

Sunday
13

Notes

MARCH

Monday
14

Tuesday
15

Wednesday
16

Thursday
17

St. Patrick's Day

MARCH

Friday
18

Saturday
19

Sunday
20

Notes

MARCH

Monday
21

Tuesday
22

Wednesday
23

Thursday
24

MARCH

Friday
25

Saturday
26

Sunday
27

Daylight Saving Time Starts / Mothering Sunday

Notes

APRIL

Things to do this month

Goals

Notes

MARCH

Monday
28

Tuesday
29

Wednesday
30

Thursday
31

APRIL

Friday
1

Saturday
2

Ramadan Begins

Sunday
3

Notes

APRIL

Monday
4

Tuesday
5

Wednesday
6

Thursday
7

APRIL

Friday
8

Saturday
9

Sunday
10

Notes

APRIL

Monday
11

Tuesday
12

Wednesday
13

Thursday
14

APRIL

Friday
15

Good Friday / Passover Begins

Saturday
16

Sunday
17

Easter Sunday

Notes

APRIL

Monday
18

Easter Monday

Tuesday
19

Wednesday
20

Thursday
21

APRIL

Friday
22

Saturday
23

St. George's Day

Sunday
24

Notes

WITCH
IN TRAINING

MAY

Things to do this month

Goals

Notes

APRIL

Monday
25

Tuesday
26

Wednesday
27

Thursday
28

APR/MAY

Friday

29

....

Saturday

30

....

Sunday

1

....

Notes

MAY

Monday
2

Early May Bank Holiday

....

Tuesday
3

....

Wednesday
4

....

Thursday
5

MAY

6

7

8

Notes

MAY

Monday
9

Tuesday
10

Wednesday
11

Thursday
12

MAY

Friday

13

Saturday

14

Sunday

15

Notes

MAY

Monday
16

Tuesday
17

Wednesday
18

Thursday
19

MAY

Notes

MAY

Monday
23

Tuesday
24

Wednesday
25

Thursday
26

MAY

Friday

27

Saturday

28

Sunday

29

Notes

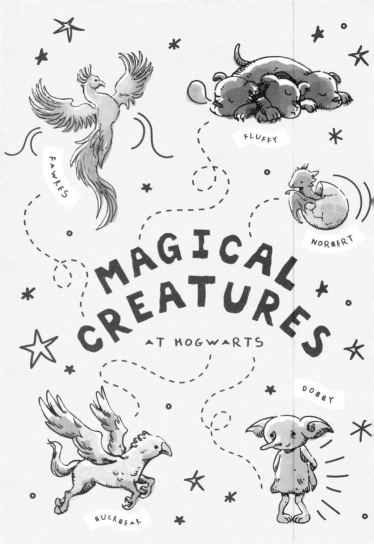

JUNE

Things to do this month

Goals

Notes

MAY/JUN

Monday
30

Tuesday
31

Wednesday
1

Thursday
2

Queen's Platinum Jubilee Bank Holiday

JUNE

Queen's Platinum Jubilee Bank Holiday

Notes

JUNE

Monday
6

Tuesday
7

Wednesday
8

Thursday
9

JUNE

Notes

JUNE

Monday
13

Tuesday
14

Wednesday
15

Thursday
16

JUNE

Friday
17

Saturday
18

Sunday
19

Father's Day

Notes

JUNE

Monday
20

Tuesday
21

Wednesday
22

Thursday
23

JUNE

24

25

26

Notes

JULY

Things to do this month

Goals

Notes

JUNE

Monday
27

Tuesday
28

Wednesday
29

Thursday
30

JULY

Friday
1

Saturday
2

Sunday
3

Notes

JULY

Monday
4

Tuesday
5

Wednesday
6

Thursday
7

JULY

Notes

JULY

Monday
11

Tuesday
12

Battle of the Boyne (Northern Ireland)

Wednesday
13

Thursday
14

JULY

Notes

JULY

Monday
18

Tuesday
19

Wednesday
20

Thursday
21

JULY

Notes

JULY

Monday
25

Tuesday
26

Wednesday
27

Thursday
28

JULY

Friday
29

Islamic New Year Begins

Saturday
30

Sunday
31

Notes

CLASSES

AT HOGWARTS

AUGUST

Things to do this month

Goals

Notes

AUGUST

Monday
1

Summer Bank Holiday (Scotland)

Tuesday
2

Wednesday
3

Thursday
4

AUGUST

Friday
5

*

Saturday
6

Sunday
7

Notes

AUGUST

Monday
8

Tuesday
9

Wednesday
10

Thursday
11

AUGUST

Friday
12

*

Saturday
13

o

Sunday
14

★

Notes

AUGUST

Monday
15

Tuesday
16

Wednesday
17

Thursday

18

AUGUST

*

o

*

Notes

*

o

AUGUST

Monday
22

Tuesday
23

Wednesday
24

Thursday
25

AUGUST

Friday
26

*

Saturday
27

○

Sunday
28

★

Notes

SEPTEMBER

Things to do this month

Goals

Notes

AUG/SEP

Monday
29

Summer Bank Holiday (ENG, NIR, WAL)

Tuesday
30

Wednesday
31

Thursday
1

SEPTEMBER

Friday
2

Saturday
3

Sunday
4

Notes

SEPTEMBER

Monday
5

Tuesday
6

Wednesday
7

Thursday
8

SEPTEMBER

Friday
9

Saturday
10

Sunday
11

Notes

SEPTEMBER

Monday
12

Tuesday
13

Wednesday
14

Thursday
15

SEPTEMBER

Friday
16

Saturday
17

Sunday
18

Notes

SEPTEMBER

Monday
19

Tuesday
20

Wednesday
21

The United Nations International Day of Peace

Thursday
22

SEPTEMBER

Friday
23

Saturday
24

Sunday
25

Rosh Hashanah (Jewish New Year) Begins

Notes

OCTOBER

Things to do this month

Goals

Notes

SEPTEMBER

Monday
26

Tuesday
27

Wednesday
28

Thursday
29

SEP/OCT

Friday
30

Saturday
1

Sunday
2

Notes

OCTOBER

Monday
3

*

Tuesday
4

Yom Kippur Begins *

Wednesday
5

o

Thursday
6

*
o

OCTOBER

Friday
7

Saturday
8

Sunday
9

Notes

OCTOBER

Monday
10

World Mental Health Day

Tuesday
11

Wednesday
12

Thursday
13

OCTOBER

Friday
14

Saturday
15

Sunday
16

Notes

OCTOBER

Monday
17

Tuesday
18

Wednesday
19

Thursday
20

OCTOBER

Friday
21

Saturday
22

Sunday
23

Notes

OCTOBER

Monday
24

Diwali

....

Tuesday
25

....

Wednesday
26

....

Thursday
27

OCTOBER

Friday
28

Saturday
29

Sunday
30

Daylight Saving Time Ends

Notes

NOVEMBER

Things to do this month

Goals

Notes

OCT/NOV

Monday
31

Halloween

Tuesday
1

Wednesday
2

Thursday
3

NOVEMBER

Friday
4

Saturday
5

Guy Fawkes Night

Sunday
6

Notes

NOVEMBER

Monday
7

Tuesday
8

Wednesday
9

Thursday
10

Friday
11

Saturday
12

Sunday
13

Remembrance Sunday

Notes

NOVEMBER

Monday
14

Tuesday
15

Wednesday
16

Thursday
17

NOVEMBER

Friday
18

Saturday
19

Sunday
20

Notes

NOVEMBER

Monday
21

Tuesday
22

Wednesday
23

Thursday
24

NOVEMBER

Friday
25

Saturday
26

Sunday
27

Notes

POTIONS
AT HOGWARTS

DECEMBER

Things to do this month

Goals

Notes

NOV/DEC

Monday
28

Tuesday
29

Wednesday
30

St. Andrew's Day (Scotland)

Thursday
1

DECEMBER

Friday
2

Saturday
3

Sunday
4

Notes

DECEMBER

Monday
5

Tuesday
6

Wednesday
7

Thursday
8

DECEMBER

Friday
9

Saturday
10

Sunday
11

Notes

DECEMBER

Monday
12

Tuesday
13

Wednesday
14

Thursday
15

DECEMBER

Friday
16

Saturday
17

Sunday
18

Notes

DECEMBER

Monday
19

Tuesday
20

Wednesday
21

Thursday
22

DECEMBER

Friday
23

saturday
24

Sunday
25

christmas Day

Notes

DECEMBER

Monday
26

Boxing Day

....

Tuesday
27

Bank Holiday

....

Wednesday
28

....

Thursday
29

DEC 22/JAN 23 *

Friday
30

*

Saturday
31

New Year's Eve

Sunday
1

New Year's Day

Notes

2023

JANUARY
M	T	W	T	F	S	S
						1
2	3	4	5	6	7	8
9	10	11	12	13	14	15
16	17	18	19	20	21	22
23	24	25	26	27	28	29
30	31					

FEBRUARY
M	T	W	T	F	S	S
		1	2	3	4	5
6	7	8	9	10	11	12
13	14	15	16	17	18	19
20	21	22	23	24	25	26
27	28					

MARCH
M	T	W	T	F	S	S
		1	2	3	4	5
6	7	8	9	10	11	12
13	14	15	16	17	18	19
20	21	22	23	24	25	26
27	28	29	30	31		

APRIL
M	T	W	T	F	S	S
					1	2
3	4	5	6	7	8	9
10	11	12	13	14	15	16
17	18	19	20	21	22	23
24	25	26	27	28	29	30

MAY
M	T	W	T	F	S	S
1	2	3	4	5	6	7
8	9	10	11	12	13	14
15	16	17	18	19	20	21
22	23	24	25	26	27	28
29	30	31				

JUNE
M	T	W	T	F	S	S
			1	2	3	4
5	6	7	8	9	10	11
12	13	14	15	16	17	18
19	20	21	22	23	24	25
26	27	28	29	30		

JULY
M	T	W	T	F	S	S
					1	2
3	4	5	6	7	8	9
10	11	12	13	14	15	16
17	18	19	20	21	22	23
24	25	26	27	28	29	30
31						

AUGUST
M	T	W	T	F	S	S
	1	2	3	4	5	6
7	8	9	10	11	12	13
14	15	16	17	18	19	20
21	22	23	24	25	26	27
28	29	30	31			

SEPTEMBER
M	T	W	T	F	S	S
				1	2	3
4	5	6	7	8	9	10
11	12	13	14	15	16	17
18	19	20	21	22	23	24
25	26	27	28	29	30	

OCTOBER
M	T	W	T	F	S	S
						1
2	3	4	5	6	7	8
9	10	11	12	13	14	15
16	17	18	19	20	21	22
23	24	25	26	27	28	29
30	31					

NOVEMBER
M	T	W	T	F	S	S
		1	2	3	4	5
6	7	8	9	10	11	12
13	14	15	16	17	18	19
20	21	22	23	24	25	26
27	28	29	30			

DECEMBER
M	T	W	T	F	S	S
				1	2	3
4	5	6	7	8	9	10
11	12	13	14	15	16	17
18	19	20	21	22	23	24
25	26	27	28	29	30	31

ESSENTIALS

AT HOGWARTS

☆ MY FRIENDS ☆

Name:

Address:

Tel:

Mob:

Email:

Name:

Address:

Tel:

Mob:

Email:

MY FRIENDS

Name:
....

Address:
....
....
....

Tel:
....

Mob:
....

Email:
....

Name:
....

Address:
....
....
....

Tel:
....

Mob:
....

Email:
....

☆ MY FRIENDS ☆

Name:
....
Address:
....

....
Tel:
....
Mob:
....
Email:
....

Name:
....
Address:
....

....
Tel:
....
Mob:
....
Email:
....

MY FRIENDS

Name:

Address:

Tel:

Mob:

Email:

Name:

Address:

Tel:

Mob:

Email:

NOTES

NOTES

NOTES

NOTES

NOTES

NOTES